Robert O'Leary

My Confirmation Year

VERITAS

First published 1997 by
Veritas Publications
7–8 Lower Abbey Street
Dublin 1
publications@veritas.ie
www.veritas.ie

ISBN 978 1 85390 313 7

26th printing 2020

A catalogue record for this book is available from the British Library

Illustrations by Mary Cawley
Cover design by Bill Bolger
Printed in the Republic of Ireland by Walsh Colour Print, Kerry

Veritas books are printed on paper made from the wood pulp of managed forests. For every tree felled, at least one tree is planted, thereby renewing natural resources.

For Evelyn, Aislinn and Aidan

with thanks to
all those teachers whose constructive
comments helped me in compiling
this material, and to the pupils
of Sacred Heart SNS, Killinarden,
Tallaght, Dublin 24, who inspired it

A Note for Parents and Teachers

Confirmation Year marks one of the most important years in primary school for every child. It is a year characterised by considerable excitement, challenge and hard work. In particular, it is characterised by enormous growth and development in many different ways: physical, intellectual, emotional and spiritual. This souvenir scrapbook reflects this development and provides many opportunities for children to express their thoughts and feelings, and to focus in a concrete way on the important issues in their lives.

A number of the topics are directly related to what the child will be learning in school, as part of preparation for Confirmation. Others encourage the children to reflect on developments and occasions in their lives, past, present and future. The book provides opportunities for the children to reflect on and examine themselves as individuals, their relationships with others and with Christ, and the challenges and possibilities that lie ahead.

As with all aspects of parenting, the support and security provided by parental involvement is crucial to the child's sense of development and self-esteem. You can contribute to this process in a very positive way by helping the child to work through the scrapbook in any way you can; by talking about the issues that arise, commenting on how the work is progressing and providing resources as required. If you do this, the end result will be a treasured memento which your child will keep for many years to come, long after Confirmation.

For the teacher, this book is intended as a classroom resource, flexible and non-prescriptive in nature. Each pupil can stamp his or her personality on the book with the use of colour. At the end of the year, each scrapbook will be as individual as its owner. A number of blank pages have been included at the back of the book for work to be prescribed at the teacher's discretion. Similarly, the empty spaces on many pages are intended for the pupils' own artwork or photographs, cuttings etc., at the teacher's discretion. I hope the souvenir scrapbook will serve as a constructive way for teachers to provide a means for children to focus on the issues and topics that matter, and to be a vehicle for making Confirmation Year as relevant, as meaningful and as memorable in the lives of the pupils as it deserves to be.

Robert O'Leary

This Souvenir Scrapbook
of my Confirmation Year
belongs to

And was begun on

Pupil Profile

Name

_____

Address

_____

Date of Birth

Teacher

School

_____

Eye Colour   Hair Colour

_____   _____

My Baptism

Date

_____

Venue

_____

My Godparents

_____

_____

I was baptised by

_____

News Headlines of the Year

September

_____
_____
_____
_____
_____

October

_____
_____
_____
_____
_____

November

_____
_____
_____
_____
_____

December

_____
_____
_____
_____
_____

January

_____
_____
_____

News Headlines of the Year

February

_____

_____

_____

_____

_____

March

_____

_____

_____

_____

_____

April

_____

_____

_____

_____

_____

May

_____

_____

_____

_____

_____

June

_____

_____

_____

_____

Growing Up

When I was a baby…
_____
_____
_____
_____
_____
_____

When I was three years old…
_____
_____
_____
_____
_____
_____

When I was seven years old…
_____
_____
_____
_____

Now that I am…
_____
_____
_____
_____

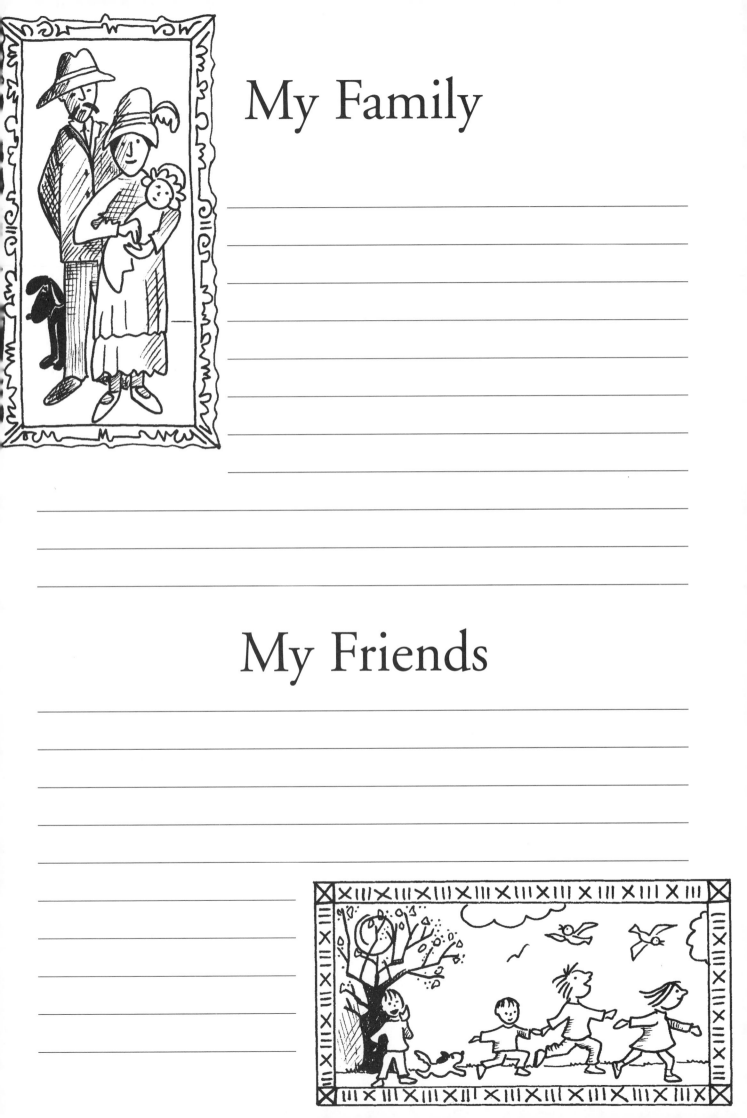

My Family

_____

_____

_____

_____

_____

_____

_____

_____

_____

_____

My Friends

_____

_____

_____

_____

_____

_____

_____

_____

My Talents

_____

_____

_____

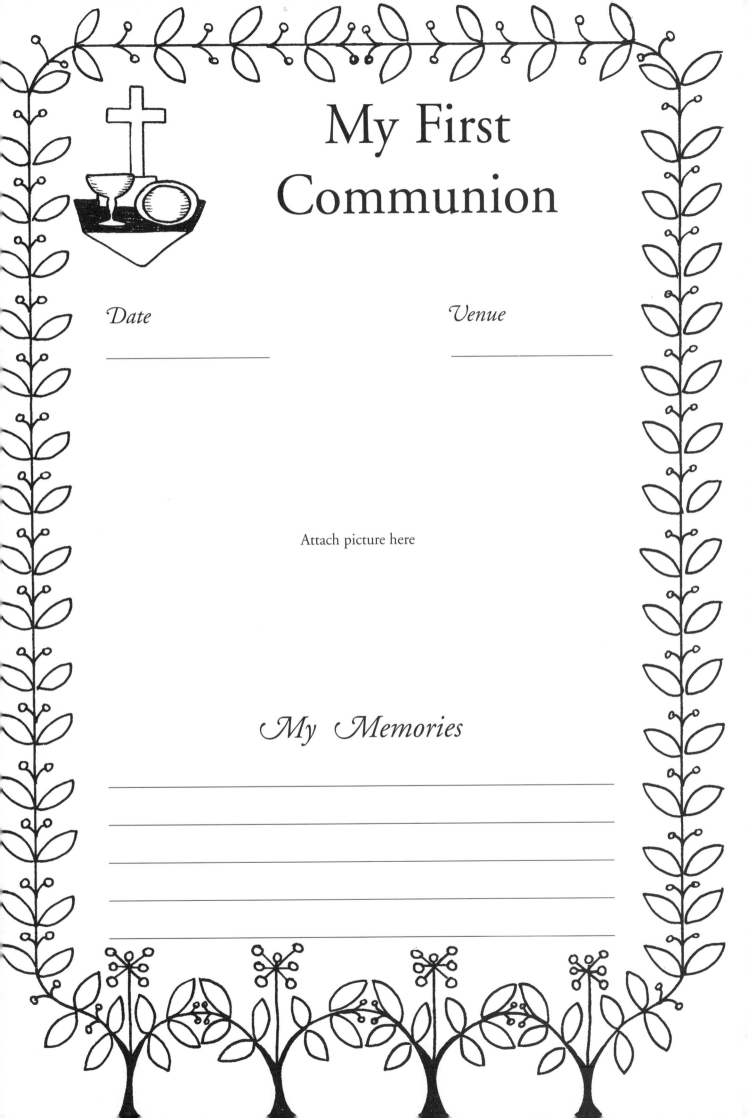

My First Communion

Date

Venue

Attach picture here

My Memories

God speaks to us
in the beauty of Creation

Favourite Things

When Jesus was a Boy

_____

_____

_____

_____

_____

_____

_____

_____

_____

_____

_____

_____

_____

_____

_____

Morning Prayer

_____

_____

_____

_____

_____

_____

_____

Night Prayer

_____

_____

_____

_____

_____

_____

_____

Where I Live

_____

_____

_____

_____

_____

_____

_____

_____

_____

_____

_____

_____

_____

_____

_____

_____

The Beatitudes

My School

Milestones in my Life

Date	Age	Event

My Favourite Biblical Story

_____

_____

_____

_____

_____

_____

_____

_____

_____

_____

_____

_____

_____

_____

_____

_____

_____

_____

_____

_____

The Seven Sacraments

_____

_____

_____

_____

_____

_____

My Christmas

The Ten Commandments

1. _____
   _____

2. _____
   _____

3. _____
   _____

4. _____
   _____

5. _____
   _____

6. _____
   _____

7. _____
   _____

8. _____

9. _____
   _____

10. _____
    _____

The Good Samaritan

_____

_____

_____

_____

_____

_____

_____

_____

_____

_____

_____

_____

_____

_____

My Hopes for the Future

_____

_____

_____

_____

_____

_____

_____

_____

_____

_____

_____

_____

_____

_____

_____

The Last Supper

_____

_____

_____

_____

_____

_____

_____

_____

_____

_____

_____

_____

_____

_____

_____

Jesus is Crucified

Easter –
A time of new life

The People
I most admire

Pentecost

_____

_____

_____

_____

_____

_____

_____

_____

_____

_____

_____

_____

_____

_____

_____

_____

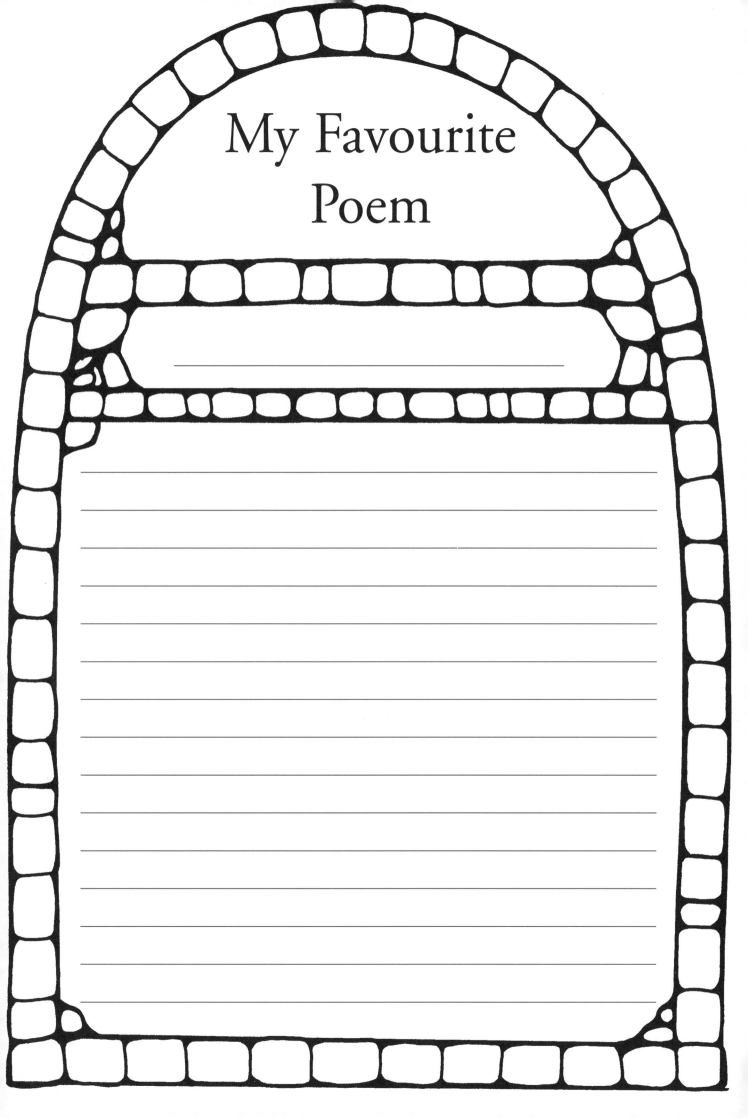

My Favourite
Poem

_____

Our School Outing

Date: _____

Venue: _____

_____
_____
_____
_____
_____
_____
_____
_____
_____
_____
_____
_____
_____

The Fruits of the Holy Spirit

_____

_____   _____

_____   _____

_____   _____

_____

The Gifts of the Holy Spirit

_____   _____

_____   _____

_____

Mary
the Mother of Jesus

The Mysteries
of the Rosary

Joyful Mysteries

_____
_____
_____
_____

Sorrowful Mysteries

_____
_____
_____
_____

Prayer to Mary

_____
_____
_____
_____
_____
_____
_____
_____

Glorious Mysteries

_____
_____
_____
_____

Mysteries of Light

_____
_____
_____
_____

What Being Confirmed Means to Me

_____

_____

_____

_____

_____

_____

_____

_____

_____

_____

_____

_____

_____

_____

_____

_____

_____

_____

_____

_____

_____

The Confirmation Pledge

_____

_____

_____

_____

_____

_____

_____

_____

_____

Prayer to the Holy Spirit

Come, Holy Spirit,
fill the hearts of your faithful,
and kindle in them
the fire of your love.
Send forth your spirit
and they shall be created,
and you will renew
the face of the earth.

Ceremony of Light

Date:

_____

Venue:

_____

Celebrant:

_____

Accompanying me were:

_____

_____

_____

_____

My Confirmation Day

Date:

_____

My Sponsor:

_____

Venue:

_____

I was confirmed by:

_____

My Confirmation Name

_____

Also present were

_____

Be Sealed with the Gift of the Holy Spirit

Autographs

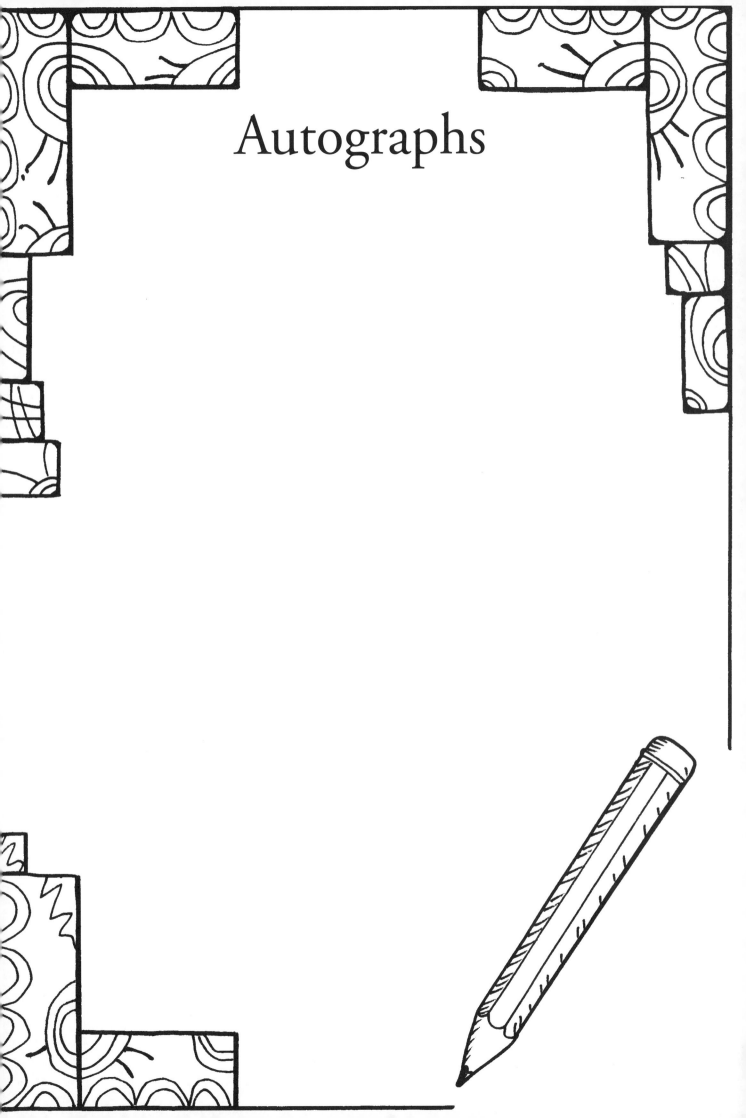

Photographs